MATHEMATICAL
FORMULAE

Third edition
Compiled by J.O. Bird & A.J.C. May

LONGMAN

Pearson Education Limited
Edinburgh Gate, Harlow
Essex CM20 2JE, England
and Associated Companies throughout the world

© Pearson Education Limited 1999

The right of J.O. Bird & A.J.C. May to be identified as authors of this work has been asserted by them in accordance with the Copyright, Designs and Patents Act 1988

First published 1979
Second edition 1993
Third edition 1999

British Library Cataloguing in Publication Data
A catalogue entry for this title is available from the British Library

ISBN 0-582-40448-7

Set by 35 in Times 10/12 and Gill Sans
Produced by Longman Singapore (Pte)
Printed in Singapore

CONTENTS

PREFACE

It is widely recognized that there is little value in requiring students to memorize large amounts of routine formulae.

This booklet provides students with a readily accessible reference to the mathematical formulae which they need during their studies.

The mathematical formulae given are relevant to NVQ, GNVQ, BTEC Edexel and CGLI courses in electrical, electronic, mechanical, production and general engineering, construction, maritime studies and science.

The formulae presented are appropriate for engineering mathematics modules at National Certificate and HNC/D, early year engineering degree courses, as well as for students studying GCSE and A-level courses.

In this third edition of *Mathematical Formulae*, extra material has been added to most sections, including further statistical tables.

John O. Bird
Portsmouth University/Highbury College

ALGEBRA

Laws of indices

$$a^m \times a^n = a^{m+n}$$

$$\frac{a^m}{a^n} = a^{m-n}$$

$$(a^m)^n = a^{mn}$$

$$a^{\frac{m}{n}} = \sqrt[n]{a^m}$$

$$a^{-n} = \frac{1}{a^n}$$

$$a^0 = 1$$

Definition of a logarithm

If $y = a^x$ then $x = \log_a y$

Laws of logarithms

$$\log(A \times B) = \log A + \log B$$

$$\log\left(\frac{A}{B}\right) = \log A - \log B$$

$$\log A^n = n \times \log A$$

Change of base

$$\log_a y = \frac{\log_b y}{\log_b a}$$

$$\ln y = \frac{\lg y}{\lg e} = 2.3026 \lg y$$

Quadratic formula

If $ax^2 + bx + c = 0$, then $x = \dfrac{-b \pm \sqrt{(b^2 - 4ac)}}{2a}$

Partial fractions

Provided that the numerator $f(x)$ is of less degree than the relevant denominator, the following identities are typical examples of the form of partial fraction used:

$$\frac{f(x)}{(x + a)(x + b)(x + c)} \equiv \frac{A}{(x + a)} + \frac{B}{(x + b)} + \frac{C}{(x + c)}$$

$$\frac{f(x)}{(x - a)^3(x + b)} \equiv \frac{A}{(x - a)} + \frac{B}{(x - a)^2} + \frac{C}{(x - a)^3} + \frac{D}{(x + b)}$$

$$\frac{f(x)}{(ax^2 + bx + c)(x - d)} \equiv \frac{Ax + B}{(ax^2 + bx + c)} + \frac{C}{(x - d)}$$

Factor theorem

If $x = a$ is a root of the equation $f(x) = 0$,

then $(x - a)$ is a factor of $f(x)$

Remainder theorem

If $(ax^2 + bx + c)$ is divided by $(x - p)$,

then the remainder will be: $ap^2 + bp + c$

or

If $(ax^3 + bx^2 + cx + d)$ is divided by $(x - p)$,

then the remainder will be: $ap^3 + bp^2 + cp + d$

Newton-Raphson iterative method

If r_1 is the approximate value for a real root of the equation $f(x) = 0$, then a closer approximation to the root r_2 is generally given by:

$$r_2 = r_1 - \frac{f(r_1)}{f'(r_1)}$$

SERIES

Binomial series

$$(a + b)^n = a^n + na^{n-1}b + \frac{n(n-1)}{2!}a^{n-2}b^2 + \frac{n(n-1)(n-2)}{3!}a^{n-3}b^3 + \ldots$$

$$(1 + x)^n = 1 + nx + \frac{n(n-1)}{2!}x^2 + \frac{n(n-1)(n-2)}{3!}x^3 + \ldots$$

(valid for $-1 < x < 1$)

Maclaurin's theorem

$$f(x) = f(0) + x f'(0) + \frac{x^2}{2!} f''(0) + \ldots$$

Taylor's theorem

$$f(a + h) = f(a) + h f'(a) + \frac{h^2}{2!} f''(a) + \ldots$$

Exponential series

$$e^x = 1 + x + \frac{x^2}{2!} + \frac{x^3}{3!} + \ldots \text{ (valid for all values of } x)$$

Logarithmic series

$$\ln(1 + x) = x - \frac{x^2}{2} + \frac{x^3}{3} - \frac{x^4}{4} + \ldots \text{ (valid for } -1 < x < 1)$$

Trigonometrical series

$$\sin x = x - \frac{x^3}{3!} + \frac{x^5}{5!} - \frac{x^7}{7!} + \ldots \text{ (valid for all values of } x)$$

$$\cos x = 1 - \frac{x^2}{2!} + \frac{x^4}{4!} - \frac{x^6}{6!} + \ldots \text{ (valid for all values of } x)$$

Hyperbolic series

$$\sinh x = x + \frac{x^3}{3!} + \frac{x^5}{5!} + \frac{x^7}{7!} + \ldots \text{ (valid for all values of } x)$$

$$\cosh x = 1 + \frac{x^2}{2!} + \frac{x^4}{4!} + \frac{x^6}{6!} + \ldots \text{ (valid for all values of } x)$$

Arithmetic progression

If a = first term, d = common difference and n = number of terms, then the arithmetic progression is: $a, a + d, a + 2d, \ldots$

The n'th term is: $a + (n - 1)d$

Sum of n terms, $S_n = \dfrac{n}{2}[2a + (n - 1)d]$

$$= \dfrac{n}{2}(a + l) \text{ where } l \text{ is the last term}$$

Geometric progression

If a = first term, r = common ratio and n = number of terms, then the geometric progression is: $a, ar, ar^2, \ldots$

The n'th term is ar^{n-1}

Sum of n terms, $S_n = \dfrac{a(1 - r^n)}{(1 - r)}$ or $\dfrac{a(r^n - 1)}{(r - 1)}$

If $-1 < r < 1$, $S_\infty = \dfrac{a}{(1 - r)}$

COMPLEX NUMBERS

$z = a + jb = r(\cos\theta + j\sin\theta) = r \angle \theta = r\,e^{j\theta}$, where $j^2 = -1$

Modulus, $r = |z| = \sqrt{(a^2 + b^2)}$

Argument, $\theta = \arg z = \arctan\dfrac{b}{a}$

Addition	$(a + jb) + (c + jd) = (a + c) + j(b + d)$
Subtraction	$(a + jb) - (c + jd) = (a - c) + j(b - d)$
Complex equations	If $m + jn = p + jq$ then $m = p$ and $n = q$
Multiplication	$z_1 z_2 = r_1 r_2 \angle (\theta_1 + \theta_2)$
Division	$\dfrac{z_1}{z_2} = \dfrac{r_1}{r_2} \angle (\theta_1 - \theta_2)$
De Moivre's theorem	$[r \angle \theta]^n = r^n \angle n\theta = r^n(\cos n\theta + j\sin n\theta)$

cos nθ and sin nθ in terms of powers of cos θ and sin θ

$$\cos n\theta = \cos^n\theta - \dfrac{n(n - 1)}{2!}\cos^{n-2}\theta\,\sin^2\theta$$

$$+ \dfrac{n(n - 1)(n - 2)(n - 3)}{4!}\cos^{n-4}\theta\,\sin^4\theta - \ldots$$

$$\sin n\theta = n\cos^{n-1}\theta\sin\theta - \frac{n(n-1)(n-2)}{3!}\cos^{n-3}\theta\sin^3\theta$$

$$+ \frac{n(n-1)(n-2)(n-3)(n-4)}{5!}\cos^{n-5}\theta\sin^5\theta - \ldots$$

$\cos^n\theta$ and $\sin^n\theta$ in terms of sines and cosines of multiples of θ

If $z = (\cos\theta + j\sin\theta)$ then:

$$\cos^n\theta = \frac{1}{2^n}\left(z + \frac{1}{z}\right)^n \qquad \left(z^n + \frac{1}{z^n}\right) = 2\cos n\theta$$

$$\sin^n\theta = \frac{1}{j^n 2^n}\left(z - \frac{1}{z}\right)^n \qquad \left(z^n - \frac{1}{z^n}\right) = 2j\sin n\theta$$

GEOMETRY

Equations of a straight line

$$y = mx + c$$

$$y - y_1 = m(x - x_1)$$

Reduction of equations to linear form

If ... then ...	Vertical axis	Gradient	Horizontal axis	Intercept on vertical axis
$y = ax^n$	$\lg y$	$= n$	$\lg x$	$+\, \lg a$
$y = ab^x$	$\lg y$	$= \lg b$	x	$+\, \lg a$
$y = ae^{kx}$	$\ln y$	$= k$	x	$+\, \ln a$
$y = ax^n + bx^{n-1}$	$\dfrac{y}{x^{n-1}}$	$= a$	x	$+\, b$

Equation of a circle

Centre at origin, radius r

$$x^2 + y^2 = r^2$$

Centre at (a, b), radius r

$$(x - a)^2 + (y - b)^2 = r^2$$

Equations of curves

Parabola

$$y = ax^2 + bx + c$$

$$y^2 = 4ac$$

Ellipse, centre at origin, semi-axes a and b

$$\frac{x^2}{a^2} + \frac{y^2}{b^2} = 1$$

Hyperbola

$$\frac{x^2}{a^2} - \frac{y^2}{b^2} = 1$$

Rectangular hyperbola

$$xy = c^2$$

Theorem of Pythagoras

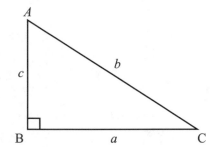

$$b^2 = a^2 + c^2$$

Centroids of common shapes

Rectangle
Centroid lies at the intersection of the diagonals

Triangle
Centroid lies at a point $\frac{h}{3}$ from the base (h = perpendicular height)

Circle
Centroid lies at its centre

Semicircle
Centroid lies on the centre line at a distance of $\frac{4r}{3\pi}$ from the diameter (r = radius)

First moment of area

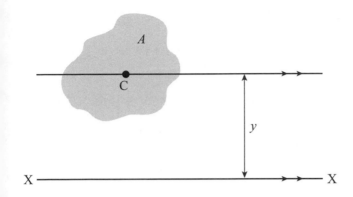

If C is the centroid of area A then:

First moment of area about XX = Ay

Radian measure

2π radians = 360 degrees

BOOLEAN ALGEBRA

Laws and rules of Boolean algebra

Commutative laws
$$A + B = B + A$$
$$A \cdot B = B \cdot A$$

Associative laws
$$A + B + C = (A + B) + C$$
$$A \cdot B \cdot C = (A \cdot B) \cdot C$$

Distributive laws
$$A \cdot (B + C) = A \cdot B + A \cdot C$$
$$A + (B \cdot C) = (A + B) \cdot (A + C)$$

Sum rules
$$A + \overline{A} = 1$$
$$A + 1 = 1$$
$$A + 0 = A$$
$$A + A = A$$

Product rules
$$A \cdot \overline{A} = 0$$
$$A \cdot 0 = 0$$
$$A \cdot 1 = A$$
$$A \cdot A = A$$

Absorption rules	$A + A \cdot B = A$
	$A \cdot (A + B) = A$
	$A + \overline{A} \cdot B = A + B$
De Morgan's laws	$\overline{A + B} = \overline{A} \cdot \overline{B}$
	$\overline{A \cdot B} = \overline{A} + \overline{B}$

LINEAR AND ANGULAR VELOCITY

If v = linear velocity (m/s), s = displacement (m), t = time (s), n = speed of revolution (rev/s), θ = angle (rad), ω = angular velocity (rad/s), r = radius of circle (m) then:

$$v = \frac{s}{t} \qquad \omega = \frac{\theta}{t} = 2\pi n \qquad v = \omega r$$

$$\text{Centripetal force} = \frac{mv^2}{r} \quad \text{where } m = \text{mass of rotating object}$$

AREAS AND VOLUMES

Areas of plane figures

Rectangle

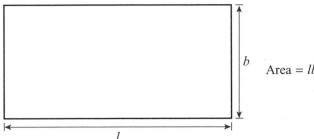

Area = lb

Parallelogram

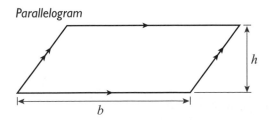

Area = bh

Trapezium

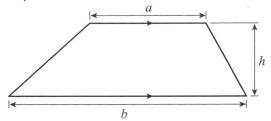

h Area $= \dfrac{1}{2}(a + b)h$

Triangle

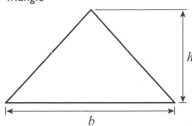

h Area $= \dfrac{1}{2}bh$

Circle

Area $= \pi r^2$

Circumference $= 2\pi r$

Sector of a circle

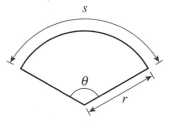

Area $= \dfrac{\theta°}{360}(\pi r^2)$

$\quad = \dfrac{1}{2}r^2\theta \qquad (\theta$ in rad.$)$

Length of arc, $s = \dfrac{\theta°}{360}(2\pi r)$

$\quad = r\theta \qquad (\theta$ in rad.$)$

Ellipse

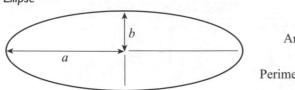

Area $= \pi ab$

Perimeter $\approx \pi(a + b)$

Volumes and surface areas of regular solids

Rectangular prism (or cuboid)

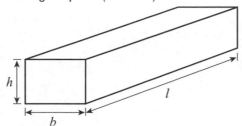

Volume $= lbh$

Surface area $= 2(bh + hl + lb)$

Cylinder

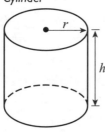

Volume $= \pi r^2 h$

Total surface area $= 2\pi rh + 2\pi r^2$

Pyramid

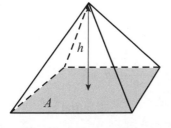

If area of base $= A$ and perpendicular height $= h$ then:

Volume $= \dfrac{1}{3} Ah$

Total surface area $=$ sum of areas of triangles forming sides plus area of base

Cone

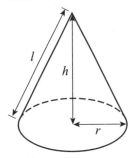

Volume $= \dfrac{1}{3}\pi r^2 h$

Curved surface area $= \pi r l$

Total surface area $= \pi r l + \pi r^2$

Frustum of a cone

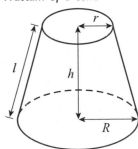

Volume $= \dfrac{1}{3}\pi h(R^2 + Rr + r^2)$

Curved surface area $= \pi l(R + r)$

Total surface area $= \pi l(R + r) + \pi r^2 + \pi R^2$

Sphere

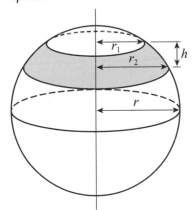

Volume $= \dfrac{4}{3}\pi r^3$

Surface area $= 4\pi r^2$

Surface area of zone $= 2\pi r h$

Volume of shaded frustum $= \dfrac{\pi h}{6}(h^2 + 3r_1^2 + 3r_2^2)$

Areas of irregular figures by approximate methods

Trapezoidal rule

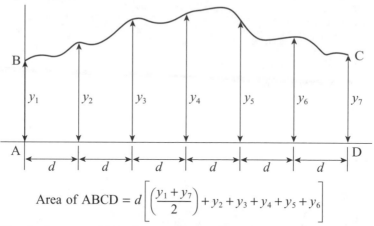

$$\text{Area of ABCD} = d\left[\left(\frac{y_1 + y_7}{2}\right) + y_2 + y_3 + y_4 + y_5 + y_6\right]$$

That is, the trapezoidal rule states that the area of an irregular figure is given by:

$$\text{Area} = \text{(width of interval)} \left[\tfrac{1}{2}\text{(first + last ordinates)} + \text{sum of remaining ordinates}\right]$$

Mid-ordinate rule

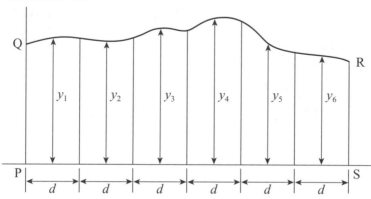

$$\text{Area of PQRS} = d[y_1 + y_2 + y_3 + y_4 + y_5 + y_6]$$

That is, the mid-ordinate rule states that the area of an irregular figure is given by:

$$\text{Area} = \text{(width of interval) (sum of mid-ordinates)}$$

Simpson's rule

To find an area such as ABCD the base AD must be divided into an even number of strips of equal width d, thus producing an odd number of ordinates, in this case 7.

$$\text{Area of ABCD} = \frac{d}{3}[(y_1 + y_7) + 4(y_2 + y_4 + y_6) + 2(y_3 + y_5)]$$

That is, Simpson's rule states that the area of an irregular figure is given by:

$$\text{Area} = \frac{1}{3}\binom{\text{width of}}{\text{interval}} \times \left[\binom{\text{first + last}}{\text{ordinate}} + 4\binom{\text{sum of even}}{\text{ordinates}} + 2\binom{\text{sum of remaining}}{\text{odd ordinates}}\right]$$

Mean or average value of a waveform

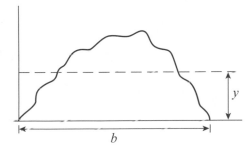

Mean or average value:

$$y = \frac{\text{area under curve}}{\text{length of base }(b)}$$

$$= \frac{\text{sum of mid-ordinates}}{\text{number of mid-ordinates}}$$

Prismoidal rule for finding volumes

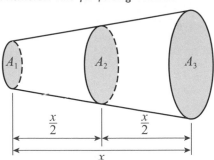

$$\text{Volume} = \frac{x}{6}[A_1 + 4A_2 + A_3]$$

Identities

$$\sec \theta = \frac{1}{\cos \theta}$$

$$\cosec \theta = \frac{1}{\sin \theta}$$

$$\cot \theta = \frac{1}{\tan \theta}$$

$$\tan \theta = \frac{\sin \theta}{\cos \theta}$$

$$\cos^2 \theta + \sin^2 \theta = 1$$

$$1 + \tan^2 \theta = \sec^2 \theta$$

$$\cot^2 \theta + 1 = \cosec^2 \theta$$

$$\sin (-\theta) = -\sin \theta$$

$$\cos (-\theta) = +\cos \theta$$

$$\tan (-\theta) = -\tan \theta$$

Trigonometric ratios for angles of any magnitude

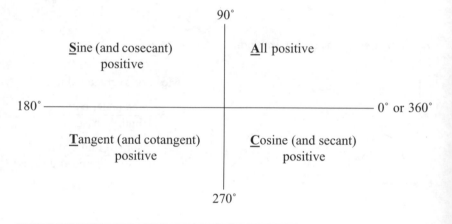

90°

Sine (and cosecant)
positive

All positive

180° ——————————————— 0° or 360°

Tangent (and cotangent)
positive

Cosine (and secant)
positive

270°

Compound angle addition and subtraction formulae

$$\sin (A + B) = \sin A \cos B + \cos A \sin B$$

$$\sin (A - B) = \sin A \cos B - \cos A \sin B$$

$$\cos (A + B) = \cos A \cos B - \sin A \sin B$$

$$\cos (A - B) = \cos A \cos B + \sin A \sin B$$

$$\tan (A + B) = \frac{\tan A + \tan B}{1 - \tan A \tan B}$$

$$\tan (A - B) = \frac{\tan A - \tan B}{1 + \tan A \tan B}$$

If $R \sin(\omega t + \alpha) = a \sin \omega t + b \cos \omega t$, then:

$$a = R \cos \alpha$$

$$b = R \sin \alpha$$

$$R = \sqrt{(a^2 + b^2)}$$

$$\alpha = \arctan \frac{b}{a}$$

Double angles

$$\sin 2A = 2 \sin A \cos A$$

$$\cos 2A = \cos^2 A - \sin^2 A = 2\cos^2 A - 1 = 1 - 2\sin^2 A$$

$$\tan 2A = \frac{2\tan A}{1 - \tan^2 A}$$

Half angles

If $\tan \dfrac{x}{2} = t$ then:

$$\sin x = \frac{2t}{1 + t^2}$$

$$\cos x = \frac{1 - t^2}{1 + t^2}$$

$$\tan x = \frac{2t}{1 - t^2}$$

Products of sines and cosines into sums or differences

$$\sin A \cos B = \tfrac{1}{2}[\sin(A + B) + \sin(A - B)]$$

$$\cos A \sin B = \tfrac{1}{2}[\sin(A + B) - \sin(A - B)]$$

$$\cos A \cos B = \tfrac{1}{2}[\cos(A + B) + \cos(A - B)]$$

$$\sin A \sin B = -\tfrac{1}{2}[\cos(A + B) - \cos(A - B)]$$

Sums or differences of sines and cosines into products

$$\sin x + \sin y = 2\sin\left(\frac{x+y}{2}\right)\cos\left(\frac{x-y}{2}\right)$$

$$\sin x - \sin y = 2\cos\left(\frac{x+y}{2}\right)\sin\left(\frac{x-y}{2}\right)$$

$$\cos x + \cos y = 2\cos\left(\frac{x+y}{2}\right)\cos\left(\frac{x-y}{2}\right)$$

$$\cos x - \cos y = -2\sin\left(\frac{x+y}{2}\right)\sin\left(\frac{x-y}{2}\right)$$

Triangle formulae

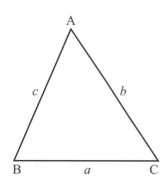

Sine rule $\quad\dfrac{a}{\sin A} = \dfrac{b}{\sin B} = \dfrac{c}{\sin C}$

Cosine rule $\quad a^2 = b^2 + c^2 - 2bc\,\cos A$

Area of any triangle

$\frac{1}{2} \times$ base $\times$ perpendicular height

$\frac{1}{2}ab\,\sin C$ or $\frac{1}{2}ac\,\sin B$ or $\frac{1}{2}bc\,\sin A$

$\sqrt{[s(s-a)(s-b)(s-c)]}$ where $s = \dfrac{a+b+c}{2}$

General sinusoidal function

If A = amplitude, ω = angular velocity = $2\pi f$ rad/s, α = angle of lead or lag (compared with $y = A \sin \omega t$) then:

$$y = A \sin (\omega t \pm \alpha)$$

$$\frac{2\pi}{\omega} = \text{periodic time } T \text{ seconds}$$

$$\frac{\omega}{2\pi} = \text{frequency, } f \text{ hertz}$$

Cartesian and polar co-ordinates

If co-ordinate $(x, y) = (r, \theta)$,

then $r = \sqrt{(x^2 + y^2)}$ and $\theta = \arctan \dfrac{y}{x}$

If co-ordinate $(r, \theta) = (x, y)$,

then $x = r \cos \theta$ and $y = r \sin \theta$

HYPERBOLIC FUNCTIONS

Definitions

$$\sinh x = \frac{e^x - e^{-x}}{2} \qquad \operatorname{cosech} x = \frac{1}{\sinh x} = \frac{2}{e^x - e^{-x}}$$

$$\cosh x = \frac{e^x + e^{-x}}{2} \qquad \operatorname{sech} x = \frac{1}{\cosh x} = \frac{2}{e^x + e^{-x}}$$

$$\tanh x = \frac{e^x - e^{-x}}{e^x + e^{-x}} \qquad \coth x = \frac{1}{\tanh x} = \frac{e^x + e^{-x}}{e^x - e^{-x}}$$

Identities

$$\cosh^2 x - \sinh^2 x = 1$$
$$1 - \tanh^2 x = \operatorname{sech}^2 x$$
$$\coth^2 x - 1 = \operatorname{cosech}^2 x$$

MATRICES AND DETERMINANTS

Matrices

If $A = \begin{pmatrix} a & b \\ c & d \end{pmatrix}$ and $B = \begin{pmatrix} e & f \\ g & h \end{pmatrix}$ then:

$$A + B = \begin{pmatrix} a+e & b+f \\ c+g & d+h \end{pmatrix}$$

$$A - B = \begin{pmatrix} a-e & b-f \\ c-g & d-h \end{pmatrix}$$

$$A \times B = \begin{pmatrix} ae+bg & af+bh \\ ce+dg & cf+dh \end{pmatrix}$$

$$A^{-1} = \frac{1}{ad-bc} \begin{pmatrix} d & -b \\ -c & a \end{pmatrix}$$

If $A = \begin{pmatrix} a_1 & b_1 & c_1 \\ a_2 & b_2 & c_2 \\ a_3 & b_3 & c_3 \end{pmatrix}$ then $A^{-1} = \dfrac{B^T}{|A|}$ (B^T = transpose of cofactors of matrix A)

Determinants

Second order

$$\begin{vmatrix} a & b \\ c & d \end{vmatrix} = ad - bc$$

Third order

$$\begin{vmatrix} a_1 & b_1 & c_1 \\ a_2 & b_2 & c_2 \\ a_3 & b_3 & c_3 \end{vmatrix} = a_1 \begin{vmatrix} b_2 & c_2 \\ b_3 & c_3 \end{vmatrix} - b_1 \begin{vmatrix} a_2 & c_2 \\ a_3 & c_3 \end{vmatrix} + c_1 \begin{vmatrix} a_2 & b_2 \\ a_3 & b_3 \end{vmatrix}$$

VECTORS

Let $\mathbf{a} = a_1\mathbf{i} + a_2\mathbf{j} + a_3\mathbf{k}$, $\mathbf{b} = b_1\mathbf{i} + b_2\mathbf{j} + b_3\mathbf{k}$ and $\mathbf{c} = c_1\mathbf{i} + c_2\mathbf{j} + c_3\mathbf{k}$

Scalar or dot product

$$\mathbf{a} \cdot \mathbf{b} = a_1b_1 + a_2b_2 + a_3b_3$$

$$|\mathbf{a}| = \sqrt{(a_1^2 + a_2^2 + a_3^2)}$$

$$\cos\theta = \frac{\mathbf{a} \cdot \mathbf{b}}{|\mathbf{a}||\mathbf{b}|}$$

Vector or cross product

$$\mathbf{a} \times \mathbf{b} = \begin{vmatrix} \mathbf{i} & \mathbf{j} & \mathbf{k} \\ a_1 & a_2 & a_3 \\ b_1 & b_2 & b_3 \end{vmatrix}$$

$$|\mathbf{a} \times \mathbf{b}| = \sqrt{[(\mathbf{a} \cdot \mathbf{a})(\mathbf{b} \cdot \mathbf{b}) - (\mathbf{a} \cdot \mathbf{b})^2]}$$

Triple scalar product of vectors

$$\mathbf{a} \cdot (\mathbf{b} \times \mathbf{c}) = \begin{vmatrix} a_1 & a_2 & a_3 \\ b_1 & b_2 & b_3 \\ c_1 & c_2 & c_3 \end{vmatrix}$$

Triple vector product

$$\mathbf{a} \times (\mathbf{b} \times \mathbf{c}) = (\mathbf{a} \cdot \mathbf{c})\mathbf{b} - (\mathbf{a} \cdot \mathbf{b})\mathbf{c}$$

$$(\mathbf{a} \times \mathbf{b}) \times \mathbf{c} = (\mathbf{c} \cdot \mathbf{a})\mathbf{b} - (\mathbf{c} \cdot \mathbf{b})\mathbf{a}$$

DIFFERENTIAL CALCULUS

Standard derivatives

y or $f(x)$	$\dfrac{dy}{dx}$ or $f'(x)$	y or $f(x)$	$\dfrac{dy}{dx}$ or $f'(x)$
ax^n	anx^{n-1}		
a^x	$a^x \ln a$	$\ln ax$	$\dfrac{1}{x}$
e^{ax}	$a\,e^{ax}$		
$\sin ax$	$a \cos ax$	$\sinh ax$	$a \cosh ax$
$\cos ax$	$-a \sin ax$	$\cosh ax$	$a \sinh ax$
$\tan ax$	$a \sec^2 ax$	$\tanh ax$	$a \operatorname{sech}^2 ax$
$\sec ax$	$a \sec ax \tan ax$	$\operatorname{sech} ax$	$-a \operatorname{sech} ax \tanh ax$
$\operatorname{cosec} ax$	$-a \operatorname{cosec} ax \cot ax$	$\operatorname{cosech} ax$	$-a \operatorname{cosech} ax \coth ax$
$\cot ax$	$-a \operatorname{cosec}^2 ax$	$\coth ax$	$-a \operatorname{cosech}^2 ax$
$\arcsin \dfrac{x}{a}$	$\dfrac{1}{\sqrt{(a^2 - x^2)}}$	$\operatorname{arcsinh} \dfrac{x}{a}$	$\dfrac{1}{\sqrt{(x^2 + a^2)}}$
$\arcsin f(x)$	$\dfrac{f'(x)}{\sqrt{[1 - f(x)^2]}}$	$\operatorname{arcsinh} f(x)$	$\dfrac{f'(x)}{\sqrt{[f(x)^2 + 1]}}$
$\arccos \dfrac{x}{a}$	$\dfrac{-1}{\sqrt{(a^2 - x^2)}}$	$\operatorname{arccosh} \dfrac{x}{a}$	$\dfrac{-1}{\sqrt{(x^2 - a^2)}}$
$\arccos f(x)$	$\dfrac{-f'(x)}{\sqrt{[1 - f(x)^2]}}$	$\operatorname{arccosh} f(x)$	$\dfrac{f'(x)}{\sqrt{[f(x)^2 - 1]}}$
$\arctan \dfrac{x}{a}$	$\dfrac{a}{a^2 + x^2}$	$\operatorname{arctanh} \dfrac{x}{a}$	$\dfrac{a}{a^2 - x^2}$
$\arctan f(x)$	$\dfrac{f'(x)}{1 + f(x)^2}$	$\operatorname{arctanh} f(x)$	$\dfrac{f'(x)}{1 - f(x)^2}$
$\operatorname{arcsec} \dfrac{x}{a}$	$\dfrac{a}{x\sqrt{(x^2 - a^2)}}$	$\operatorname{arcsech} \dfrac{x}{a}$	$\dfrac{-a}{x\sqrt{(a^2 - x^2)}}$
$\operatorname{arcsec} f(x)$	$\dfrac{f'(x)}{f(x)\sqrt{[f(x)^2 - 1]}}$	$\operatorname{arcsech} f(x)$	$\dfrac{-f'(x)}{f(x)\sqrt{[1 - f(x)^2]}}$
$\operatorname{arccosec} \dfrac{x}{a}$	$\dfrac{-a}{x\sqrt{(x^2 - a^2)}}$	$\operatorname{arccosech} \dfrac{x}{a}$	$\dfrac{-a}{x\sqrt{(x^2 + a^2)}}$
$\operatorname{arccosec} f(x)$	$\dfrac{-f'(x)}{f(x)\sqrt{[f(x)^2 - 1]}}$	$\operatorname{arccosech} f(x)$	$\dfrac{-f'(x)}{f(x)\sqrt{[f(x)^2 + 1]}}$
$\operatorname{arccot} \dfrac{x}{a}$	$\dfrac{-a}{a^2 + x^2}$	$\operatorname{arccoth} \dfrac{x}{a}$	$\dfrac{a}{a^2 - x^2}$
$\operatorname{arccot} f(x)$	$\dfrac{-f'(x)}{1 + f(x)^2}$	$\operatorname{arccoth} f(x)$	$\dfrac{f'(x)}{1 - f(x)^2}$

Product rule

When $y = uv$ and u and v are functions of x, then:

$$\frac{dy}{dx} = v\frac{du}{dx} + u\frac{dv}{dx}$$

Quotient rule

When $y = \dfrac{u}{v}$ and u and v are functions of x, then:

$$\frac{dy}{dx} = \frac{v\dfrac{du}{dx} - u\dfrac{dv}{dx}}{v^2}$$

Maximum and minimum values

If $y = f(x)$ then $\dfrac{dy}{dx} = 0$ for stationary points. Let a solution of $\dfrac{dy}{dx} = 0$ be $x = a$.

If the value of $\dfrac{d^2y}{dx^2}$ when $x = a$ is: $\quad$ *positive* $\quad$ the point is a $\quad$ *minimum* value

$\qquad\qquad\qquad\qquad\qquad\qquad\quad$ *negative* $\quad$ the point is a $\quad$ *maximum* value

$\qquad\qquad\qquad\qquad\qquad\qquad\quad$ *zero* $\qquad\;$ the point is a $\quad$ *point of inflexion*

Velocity and acceleration

If distance $x = f(t)$, then

$$\text{velocity } v = f'(t) \text{ or } \frac{dx}{dt} \qquad\qquad \text{acceleration } a = f''(t) \text{ or } \frac{d^2x}{dt^2}$$

Tangents and normals

Equation of tangent to curve $y = f(x)$ at the point (x_1, y_1) is:

$$y - y_1 = m(x - x_1) \text{ where } m = \text{gradient of curve at } (x_1, y_1)$$

Equation of normal to curve $y = f(x)$ at the point (x_1, y_1) is:

$$y - y_1 = -\frac{1}{m}(x - x_1)$$

Function of a function rule (chain rule)

If u is a function of x, then:

$$\frac{dy}{dx} = \frac{dy}{du} \times \frac{du}{dx}$$

Implicit differentiation

$$\frac{d}{dx}[f(y)] = \frac{d}{dy}[f(y)] \times \frac{dy}{dx}$$

Parametric differentiation

If x and y are both functions of θ, then:

$$\frac{dy}{dx} = \frac{\frac{dy}{d\theta}}{\frac{dx}{d\theta}} \qquad \frac{d^2y}{dx^2} = \frac{\frac{d}{d\theta}\left(\frac{dy}{dx}\right)}{\frac{dx}{d\theta}}$$

Partial differentiation

Total differential
If $z = f(u, v, \ldots)$, then the total differential dz is given by:

$$dz = \frac{\partial z}{\partial u}\,du + \frac{\partial z}{\partial v}\,dv + \ldots$$

Rate of change
If $z = f(u, v, \ldots)$ and $\frac{du}{dt}, \frac{dv}{dt}, \ldots$ denote the rate of change of $u, v, \ldots$ respectively, then the rate of change of z, $\frac{dz}{dt}$, is given by:

$$\frac{dz}{dt} = \frac{\partial z}{\partial u} \cdot \frac{du}{dt} + \frac{\partial z}{\partial v} \cdot \frac{dv}{dt} + \ldots$$

Small changes
If $z = f(x, y, \ldots)$ and $\delta x, \delta y, \ldots$ denote small changes in $x, y, \ldots$ respectively, then the corresponding change δz in z is given by:

$$\delta z \approx \frac{\partial z}{\partial x}\,\delta x + \frac{\partial z}{\partial y}\,\delta y + \ldots$$

Maxima, minima and saddle points for functions of two variables

Given $z = f(x, y)$:

Determine $\dfrac{\partial z}{\partial x}$ and $\dfrac{\partial z}{\partial y}$

Solve the simultaneous equations $\dfrac{\partial z}{\partial x} = 0$ and $\dfrac{\partial z}{\partial y} = 0$ for x and y

This gives the co-ordinates of the stationary points

Determine and evaluate $\dfrac{\partial^2 z}{\partial x^2}, \dfrac{\partial^2 z}{\partial y^2}$ and $\dfrac{\partial^2 z}{\partial x \partial y}$ for each stationary point

Evaluate $\left(\dfrac{\partial^2 z}{\partial x \partial y}\right)^2$ for each stationary point

Substitute the values of $\dfrac{\partial^2 z}{\partial x^2}$, $\dfrac{\partial^2 z}{\partial y^2}$ and $\dfrac{\partial^2 z}{\partial x \partial y}$ and evaluate the equation:

$$\Delta = \left(\frac{\partial^2 z}{\partial x \partial y}\right)^2 - \left(\frac{\partial^2 z}{\partial x^2}\right)\left(\frac{\partial^2 z}{\partial y^2}\right)$$

If $\Delta > 0$ then the stationary point is a *saddle point*

If $\Delta < 0$ and $\dfrac{\partial^2 z}{\partial x^2} < 0$ then the stationary point is a *maximum point*

If $\Delta < 0$ and $\dfrac{\partial^2 z}{\partial x^2} > 0$ then the stationary point is a *minimum point*

INTEGRAL CALCULUS

Standard integrals

y	$\int y \, dx$
ax^n	$a\dfrac{x^{n+1}}{n+1} + c$ (except where $n = -1$)
e^{ax}	$\dfrac{1}{a} e^{ax} + c$
$\dfrac{1}{x}$	$\ln x + c$
$\sin ax$	$-\dfrac{1}{a} \cos ax + c$
$\cos ax$	$\dfrac{1}{a} \sin ax + c$
$\tan ax$	$\dfrac{1}{a} \ln (\sec ax) + c$
$\sec^2 ax$	$\dfrac{1}{a} \tan ax + c$
$\operatorname{cosec}^2 ax$	$-\dfrac{1}{a} \cot ax + c$
$\sec ax \tan ax$	$\dfrac{1}{a} \sec ax + c$
$\operatorname{cosec} ax \cot ax$	$-\dfrac{1}{a} \operatorname{cosec} ax + c$

y	$\int y\,dx$	
$\sin^2 x$	$\dfrac{1}{2}\left(x - \dfrac{\sin 2x}{2}\right) + c$	(use $\cos 2x = 1 - 2\sin^2 x$)
$\cos^2 x$	$\dfrac{1}{2}\left(x + \dfrac{\sin 2x}{2}\right) + c$	(use $\cos 2x = 2\cos^2 x - 1$)
$\tan^2 x$	$\tan x - x + c$	(use $1 + \tan^2 x = \sec^2 x$)
$\cot^2 x$	$-\cot x - x + c$	(use $\cot^2 x + 1 = \operatorname{cosec}^2 x$)
$\dfrac{1}{a^2 + x^2}$	$\dfrac{1}{a}\arctan\dfrac{x}{a} + c$	(use $x = a\tan\theta$)
$\dfrac{1}{x^2 - a^2}$	$\dfrac{1}{2a}\ln\left(\dfrac{x - a}{x + a}\right) + c$	(use partial fractions)
$\dfrac{1}{a^2 - x^2}$	$\begin{cases} \dfrac{1}{2a}\ln\left(\dfrac{a + x}{a - x}\right) + c & \text{(use partial fractions)} \\ \text{or} \\ \dfrac{1}{a}\operatorname{artanh}\dfrac{x}{a} + c & \text{(use } x = a\tanh\theta\text{)} \end{cases}$	
$\dfrac{1}{\sqrt{(a^2 - x^2)}}$	$\arcsin\dfrac{x}{a} + c$	(use $x = a\sin\theta$)
$\sqrt{(a^2 - x^2)}$	$\dfrac{a^2}{2}\arcsin\dfrac{x}{a} + \dfrac{x}{2}\sqrt{(a^2 - x^2)} + c$	(use $x = a\sin\theta$)
$\dfrac{1}{\sqrt{(x^2 + a^2)}}$	$\begin{cases} \operatorname{arsinh}\dfrac{x}{a} + c & \text{(use } x = a\sinh\theta\text{)} \\ \text{or} \\ \ln\left[\dfrac{x + \sqrt{(x^2 + a^2)}}{a}\right] + c \end{cases}$	
$\sqrt{(x^2 + a^2)}$	$\dfrac{a^2}{2}\operatorname{arsinh}\dfrac{x}{a} + \dfrac{x}{2}\sqrt{(x^2 + a^2)} + c$	(use $x = a\sinh\theta$)
$\dfrac{1}{\sqrt{(x^2 - a^2)}}$	$\begin{cases} \operatorname{arcosh}\dfrac{x}{a} + c & \text{(use } x = a\cosh\theta\text{)} \\ \text{or} \\ \ln\left[\dfrac{x + \sqrt{(x^2 - a^2)}}{a}\right] + c \end{cases}$	
$\sqrt{(x^2 - a^2)}$	$\dfrac{x}{2}\sqrt{(x^2 - a^2)} - \dfrac{a^2}{2}\operatorname{arcosh}\dfrac{x}{a} + c$	(use $x = a\cosh\theta$)

Integration by parts

If u and v are both functions of x, then:

$$\int u \frac{dv}{dx}\, dx = uv - \int v \frac{du}{dx}\, dx$$

Reduction formulae

$$\int x^n e^x\, dx = I_n = x^n e^x - n I_{n-1}$$

$$\int x^n \cos x\, dx = I_n = x^n \sin x + n x^{n-1} \cos x - n(n-1) I_{n-2}$$

$$\int_0^\pi x^n \cos x\, dx = I_n = -n\pi^{n-1} - n(n-1) I_{n-2}$$

$$\int x^n \sin x\, dx = I_n = -x^n \cos x + n x^{n-1} \sin x - n(n-1) I_{n-2}$$

$$\int_0^{\pi/2} x^n \sin x\, dx = I_n = n\left(\frac{\pi}{2}\right)^{n-1} - n(n-1) I_{n-2}$$

$$\int \sin^n x\, dx = I_n = -\frac{1}{n} \sin^{n-1} x \cos x + \frac{n-1}{n} I_{n-2}$$

$$\int \cos^n x\, dx = I_n = \frac{1}{n} \cos^{n-1} x \sin x + \frac{n-1}{n} I_{n-2}$$

$$\int \tan^n x\, dx = I_n = \frac{\tan^{n-1} x}{n-1} - I_{n-2}$$

$$\int (\ln x)^n\, dx = I_n = x(\ln x)^n - n I_{n-1}$$

$$\int_0^{\pi/2} \sin^n x\, dx = \int_0^{\pi/2} \cos^n x\, dx = I_n = \frac{n-1}{n} I_{n-2}$$

Applications of integration

Area under curve

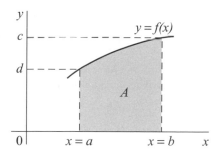

$$\text{Area, } A = \int_a^b y\,dx$$

Mean value

In the figure above the mean value of $y = f(x)$ between $x = a$ and $x = b$ is given by:

$$\text{Mean value} = \frac{1}{b-a}\int_a^b y\,dx$$

Volume of revolution

In the figure above the volume of the solid of revolution, V, obtained by rotating the curve $y = f(x)$ through one revolution is given by:

$$V = \int_a^b \pi y^2\,dx \text{ about the } x\text{-axis}$$

$$V = \int_c^d \pi x^2\,dx \text{ about the } y\text{-axis}$$

Root mean square value

In the figure above the r.m.s. value of $y = f(x)$ over the range $x = a$ to $x = b$ is given by:

$$\text{r.m.s. value} = \sqrt{\left(\frac{1}{b-a}\int_a^b y^2\,dx\right)}$$

Centroids

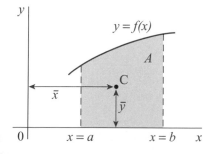

If $\bar{x}$ and $\bar{y}$ denote the co-ordinates of the centroid C of area A then:

$$\bar{x} = \frac{\displaystyle\int_a^b xy\,dx}{\displaystyle\int_a^b y\,dx} \qquad \bar{y} = \frac{\displaystyle\frac{1}{2}\int_a^b y^2\,dx}{\displaystyle\int_a^b y\,dx}$$

Theorem of Pappus (or Guldinus)

In the figure above when the curve $y = f(x)$ is rotated one revolution about the x-axis between the limits $x = a$ and $x = b$, the volume V generated is given by:

Volume, $V = 2\pi A \bar{y}$

Second moment of area

Shape	Position of axis	Second moment of area	Radius of gyration k
Rectangle length l breadth b area A	Coinciding with b	$\dfrac{bl^3}{3}$ or $A\dfrac{l^2}{3}$	$\dfrac{l}{\sqrt{3}}$
	Coinciding with l	$\dfrac{lb^3}{3}$ or $A\dfrac{b^2}{3}$	$\dfrac{b}{\sqrt{3}}$
	Through centroid, parallel to b	$\dfrac{bl^3}{12}$ or $A\dfrac{l^2}{12}$	$\dfrac{l}{\sqrt{12}}$ or $\dfrac{l}{2\sqrt{3}}$
Triangle perpendicular height h base b area A	Coinciding with base	$\dfrac{bh^3}{12}$ or $A\dfrac{h^2}{6}$	$\dfrac{h}{\sqrt{6}}$
	Through centroid, parallel to base	$\dfrac{bh^3}{36}$ or $A\dfrac{h^2}{18}$	$\dfrac{h}{\sqrt{18}}$ or $\dfrac{h}{3\sqrt{2}}$
	Through vertex, parallel to base	$\dfrac{bh^3}{4}$ or $A\dfrac{h^2}{2}$	$\dfrac{h}{\sqrt{2}}$
Circle radius r area A	Through centre, perpendicular to plane (i.e. polar axis)	$\dfrac{\pi r^4}{2}$ or $A\dfrac{r^2}{2}$	$\dfrac{r}{\sqrt{2}}$
	Coinciding with diameter	$\dfrac{\pi r^4}{4}$ or $A\dfrac{r^2}{4}$	$\dfrac{r}{2}$
	About a tangent	$\dfrac{5\pi}{4}r^4$ or $\dfrac{5}{4}Ar^2$	$\dfrac{\sqrt{5}}{2}r$
Semicircle radius r area A	Coinciding with diameter	$\dfrac{\pi r^4}{8}$ or $A\dfrac{r^2}{4}$	$\dfrac{r}{2}$

Parallel axis theorem

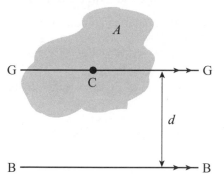

If C is the centroid of area A, then:

$$A k_{BB}^2 = A k_{GG}^2 + A d^2$$

$$k_{BB}^2 = k_{GG}^2 + d^2$$

Perpendicular axis theorem

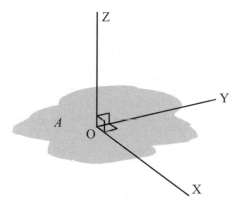

If OX and OY lie in the plane of area A, then:

$$A k_{OZ}^2 = A k_{OX}^2 + A k_{OY}^2$$

$$k_{OZ}^2 = k_{OX}^2 + k_{OY}^2$$

DIFFERENTIAL EQUATIONS

First order differential equations

If $\dfrac{dy}{dx} = f(x)$ then $y = \displaystyle\int f(x)\, dx$

If $\dfrac{dy}{dx} = f(y)$ then $\displaystyle\int dx = \int \dfrac{dy}{f(y)}$

If $\dfrac{dy}{dx} = f(x) \cdot f(y)$ then $\displaystyle\int \dfrac{dy}{f(y)} = \int f(x)\, dx$

If $\dfrac{dQ}{dt} = kQ$ then $Q = A e^{kt}$ (A and k are constants)

Homogeneous equations

If $P\dfrac{dy}{dx} = Q$, where P and Q are functions of both x and y of the same degree throughout (i.e. a *homogeneous* first order differential equation), then:

Rearrange into the form $\dfrac{dy}{dx} = \dfrac{Q}{P}$

Make the substitution $y = vx$ (where v is a function of x), from which, by the product rule:

$$\dfrac{dy}{dx} = v(1) + x\dfrac{dv}{dx}$$

Substitute for both y and $\dfrac{dy}{dx}$ in the equation $\dfrac{dy}{dx} = \dfrac{Q}{P}$

Simplify, by cancelling, and then separate the variables and solve using the $\dfrac{dy}{dx} = f(x) \cdot f(y)$ method above

Substitute $v = \dfrac{y}{x}$ to solve in terms of the original variable

Linear equations

If $\dfrac{dy}{dx} + Py = Q$, where P and Q are functions of x only (i.e. a *linear* first order differential equation), then:

Determine the integrating factor $e^{\int P dx}$

Substitute the integrating factor (I.F.) into the equation:

$$y(\text{I.F.}) = \int (\text{I.F.})Q\, dx$$

Determine the integral $\displaystyle\int (\text{I.F.})Q\, dx$

Second order differential equations

If $a\dfrac{d^2 y}{dx^2} + b\dfrac{dy}{dx} + cy = 0$ (where a, b and c are constants), then:

Rewrite the differential equation as $(aD^2 + bD + c)y = 0$

Substitute m for D and solve the auxiliary equation $am^2 + bm + c = 0$

If the roots of the auxiliary equation are:

real and different, say $m = \alpha$ and $m = \beta$, then the general solution is:

$$y = Ae^{\alpha x} + Be^{\beta x}$$

real and equal, say $m = \alpha$ twice, then the general solution is:

$$y = (Ax + B)e^{\alpha x}$$

complex, say $m = \alpha \pm j\beta$, then the general solution is:

$$y = e^{\alpha x}(A \cos \beta x + B \sin \beta x)$$

Given boundary conditions, constants A and B can be determined and the particular solution obtained

If $a\dfrac{d^2y}{dx^2} + b\dfrac{dy}{dx} + cy = f(x)$ (where a, b and c are constants), then:

Rewrite the differential equation as $(aD^2 + bD + c)y = f(x)$

Substitute m for D and solve the auxiliary equation $am^2 + bm + c = 0$

Obtain the complementary function (C.F.), u, as above

To find the particular integral, v, first assume a particular integral which is suggested by $f(x)$, but which contains undetermined coefficients (the table on the next page gives some suggested substitutions)

Substitute the suggested particular integral into the original differential equation and equate relevant coefficients to find the constants introduced

The general solution is given by:

$$y = u + v$$

Given boundary conditions, arbitrary constants in the C.F. can be determined and the particular solution obtained.

Form of particular integral for different functions

Type	Straightforward	'Snag' cases
$f(x)$ = a constant	$v = k$	$v = kx$ (used when C.F. contains a constant)
$f(x)$ = a polynomial (i.e. $f(x) = L + Mx + Nx^2 + \ldots$) where any of the coefficients may be zero	$v = a + bx + cx^2 + \ldots$	
$f(x)$ = an exponential function (i.e. $f(x) = Ae^{\alpha x}$)	$v = ke^{\alpha x}$	$v = kxe^{\alpha x}$ (used when $e^{\alpha x}$ appears in the C.F.) $v = kx^2e^{\alpha x}$ (used when $e^{\alpha x}$ and $xe^{\alpha x}$ both appear in the C.F.), and so on
$f(x)$ = a sine or cosine function (i.e. $f(x) = a \sin px + b \cos px$, where a and b may be zero)	$v = A \sin px + B \cos px$	$v = x (A \sin px + B \cos px)$ (used when $\sin px$ and/or $\cos px$ appears in the C.F.)
$f(x)$ = a sum e.g. $f(x) = 2x^2 + 5 \cos 3x$ $f(x) = x + 1 - e^{-x}$	$v = ax^2 + bx + c + d \cos 3x + e \sin 3x$ $v = ax + b + ce^{-x}$	
$f(x)$ = a product e.g. $f(x) = 3e^{2x} \sin 4x$	$v = e^{2x}(A \cos 4x + B \sin 4x)$	

Euler's method

$$y_1 = y_0 + h(y')_0$$

Euler–Cauchy method

$$y_{P_1} = y_0 + h(y')_0$$

$$y_{C_1} = y_0 + \frac{1}{2}h\left[(y')_0 + f(x_1, y_{P_1})\right]$$

LAPLACE TRANSFORMS

Standard Laplace transforms

$f(t)$	$\mathcal{L}\{f(t)\} = \displaystyle\int_0^\infty e^{-st} f(t)\, dt$
1	$\dfrac{1}{s}$
k	$\dfrac{k}{s}$
e^{at}	$\dfrac{1}{s-a}$
$\sin \omega t$	$\dfrac{\omega}{s^2 + \omega^2}$
$\cos \omega t$	$\dfrac{s}{s^2 + \omega^2}$
t	$\dfrac{1}{s^2}$
t^2	$\dfrac{2\,!}{s^3}$
t^n (n = positive integer)	$\dfrac{n\,!}{s^{n+1}}$
$\sinh \omega t$	$\dfrac{\omega}{s^2 - \omega^2}$
$\cosh \omega t$	$\dfrac{s}{s^2 - \omega^2}$
$e^{at} t^n$	$\dfrac{n\,!}{(s-a)^{n+1}}$
$e^{-at} \sin \omega t$	$\dfrac{\omega}{(s+a)^2 + \omega^2}$
$e^{-at} \cos \omega t$	$\dfrac{s+a}{(s+a)^2 + \omega^2}$
$e^{-at} \sinh \omega t$	$\dfrac{\omega}{(s+a)^2 - \omega^2}$
$e^{-at} \cosh \omega t$	$\dfrac{s+a}{(s+a)^2 - \omega^2}$

The Laplace transforms of derivatives

First derivative

$$\mathscr{L}\left\{\frac{dy}{dx}\right\} = s\mathscr{L}\{y\} - y(0)$$

where $y(0)$ is the value of y at $x = 0$

Second derivative

$$\mathscr{L}\left\{\frac{d^2y}{dx^2}\right\} = s^2\mathscr{L}\{y\} - sy\{0\} - y'(0)$$

where $y'(0)$ is the value of $\frac{dy}{dx}$ at $x = 0$

Higher derivatives

$$\mathscr{L}\left\{\frac{d^ny}{dx^n}\right\} = s^n\mathscr{L}\{y\} - s^{n-1}y(0) - s^{n-2}y'(0) \ldots - y^{n-1}(0)$$

FOURIER SERIES

Periodic functions of period 2π

If $f(x)$ is a periodic function of period 2π then its Fourier series is given by:

$$f(x) = a_0 + \sum_{n=1}^{\infty}(a_n \cos nx + b_n \sin nx)$$

where, for the range $-\pi$ to $+\pi$:

$$a_0 = \frac{1}{2\pi}\int_{-\pi}^{\pi} f(x)\,dx$$

$$a_n = \frac{1}{\pi}\int_{-\pi}^{\pi} f(x)\cos nx\,dx \qquad (n = 1, 2, 3, \ldots)$$

$$b_n = \frac{1}{\pi}\int_{-\pi}^{\pi} f(x)\sin nx\,dx \qquad (n = 1, 2, 3, \ldots)$$

Even functions

If $f(x)$ is even in the range $-\pi < x < \pi$ then $f(x) = -f(x)$ and the Fourier series has no sine terms (i.e. $b_n = 0$):

$$a_0 = \frac{1}{2\pi}\int_{-\pi}^{\pi} f(x)\,dx = \frac{1}{\pi}\int_{0}^{\pi} f(x)\,dx$$

$$a_n = \frac{1}{\pi} \int_{-\pi}^{\pi} f(x) \cos nx \, dx = \frac{2}{\pi} \int_{0}^{\pi} f(x) \cos nx \, dx$$

Odd functions

If $f(x)$ is odd in the range $-\pi < x < \pi$ then $f(-x) = -f(x)$ and the Fourier series has no cosine terms (i.e. $a_n = 0$):

$$a_0 = 0$$

$$b_n = \frac{1}{\pi} \int_{-\pi}^{\pi} f(x) \sin nx \, dx = \frac{2}{\pi} \int_{0}^{\pi} f(x) \sin nx \, dx$$

Periodic functions of period L

If $f(x)$ is a function of period L, then its Fourier series is given by:

$$f(x) = a_0 + \sum_{n=1}^{\infty} \left\{ a_n \cos\left(\frac{2\pi nx}{L}\right) + b_n \sin\left(\frac{2\pi nx}{L}\right) \right\}$$

where for the range $-\frac{L}{2}$ to $+\frac{L}{2}$:

$$a_0 = \frac{1}{L} \int_{-L/2}^{L/2} f(x) \, dx$$

$$a_n = \frac{2}{L} \int_{-L/2}^{L/2} f(x) \cos\left(\frac{2\pi nx}{L}\right) dx \qquad (n = 1, 2, 3, \dots)$$

$$b_n = \frac{2}{L} \int_{-L/2}^{L/2} f(x) \sin\left(\frac{2\pi nx}{L}\right) dx \qquad (n = 1, 2, 3, \dots)$$

Harmonic analysis

If the range 2π is divided into p equal intervals, then:

$$a_0 \approx \frac{1}{p} \sum_{k=1}^{p} y_k$$

$$a_n \approx \frac{2}{p} \sum_{k=1}^{p} y_k \cos nx_k \qquad \text{and} \qquad b_n \approx \frac{2}{p} \sum_{k=1}^{p} y_k \sin nx_k$$

Grouped data

For the class of grouped data shown shaded, the class interval is 7–8, the class limits are 7 and 8, the class midpoint is 7.5, the lower class boundary is 6.5 and the upper class boundary is 8.5

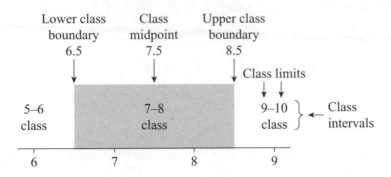

Mean, median, mode and standard deviation

If x = variate and f = frequency then:

$$\text{Mean, } \bar{x} = \frac{\Sigma f x}{\Sigma f}$$

The median is the middle term of a ranked set of data. The mode is the most commonly occurring value in a set of data.

$$\text{Standard deviation, } \sigma = \sqrt{\left[\frac{\Sigma\{f(x-\bar{x})^2\}}{\Sigma f}\right]} \text{ for a population}$$

Binomial probability distribution

If n = number in sample, p = probability of the occurrence of an event and $q = 1 - p$, then the probability of 0, 1, 2, 3, ... occurrences is given by:

$$q^n, \, nq^{n-1}p, \, \frac{n(n-1)}{2!}q^{n-2}p^2, \, \frac{n(n-1)(n-2)}{3!}q^{n-3}p^3, \ldots$$

(That is, successive terms of the $(q + p)^n$ expansion.)

$$\text{Mean, } \mu = np$$

$$\text{Standard deviation, } \sigma = \sqrt{(n\,p\,q)}$$

Poisson distribution

If λ is the expectation of the occurrence of an event, then the probability of 0, 1, 2, 3, ... occurrences is given by:

$$e^{-\lambda}, \; \lambda e^{-\lambda}, \; \lambda^2 \frac{e^{-\lambda}}{2!}, \; \lambda^3 \frac{e^{-\lambda}}{3!}, \ldots$$

Mean, $\mu = \lambda = np$

Standard deviation, $\sigma = \sqrt{\lambda}$

Product-moment formula for the linear correlation coefficient

$$\text{Coefficient of correlation, } r = \frac{\sum xy}{\sqrt{[(\sum x^2)(\sum y^2)]}}$$

where $x = X - \bar{X}$ and $y = Y - \bar{Y}$ and $(X_1, Y_1), (X_2, Y_2), \ldots$ denote a random sample from a bivariate normal distribution and $\bar{X}$ and $\bar{Y}$ are the means of the X and Y values respectively.

Symbols

Population	Number of members N_p	Mean μ	Standard deviation σ
Sample	Number of members N	Mean $\bar{x}$	Standard deviation s

Sampling distributions

Mean of sampling distribution of means $\mu_{\bar{x}}$

Standard error of means $\sigma_{\bar{x}}$

Standard error of the standard deviations σ_s

Standard error of the means

Standard error of the means of a sample distribution, i.e. the standard deviation of the means of samples, is:

$$\sigma_{\bar{x}} = \frac{\sigma}{\sqrt{N}} \sqrt{\left(\frac{N_p - N}{N_p - 1} \right)} \qquad \text{for a finite population and/or for sampling without replacement}$$

$$\sigma_{\bar{x}} = \frac{\sigma}{\sqrt{N}} \qquad \text{for an infinite population and/or for sampling with replacement}$$

The relationship between sample mean and population mean

For all possible samples of size N which are drawn from a population of size N_p:

$$\mu_{\bar{x}} = \mu$$

Estimating the mean and standard deviation of a population

Mean of a population (σ known)
The confidence coefficient for a large sample size ($N \geqslant 30$) is z_c where:

Confidence level %	Confidence coefficient z_c
99	2.58
98	2.33
96	2.05
95	1.96
90	1.645
80	1.28
50	0.6745

The confidence limits of a population mean based on sample data are given by:

$$\bar{x} \pm \frac{z_c \sigma}{\sqrt{N}} \sqrt{\left(\frac{N_p - N}{N_p - 1} \right)} \qquad \text{for a finite population of size } N_p$$

$$\bar{x} \pm \frac{z_c \sigma}{\sqrt{N}} \qquad \text{for an infinite population}$$

Mean of a population (σ unknown)
The confidence limits of a population mean based on sample data are given by:

$$\mu_{\bar{x}} \pm z_c \sigma_{\bar{x}}$$

Standard deviation of a population
The confidence limits of the standard deviation of a population based on sample data are given by:

$$s \pm z_c \sigma_s$$

Mean of a population based on a small sample size
The confidence coefficient for a small sample size ($N < 30$) is t_c which can be determined using the above table. The confidence limits of a population mean based on sample data given by:

$$\bar{x} \pm \frac{t_c \, s}{\sqrt{(N - 1)}}$$

Normal probability distribution

Partial areas under the
standardised normal curve

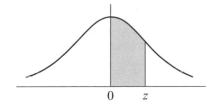

$z = \dfrac{x - \bar{x}}{\sigma}$	0	1	2	3	4	5	6	7	8	9
0.0	0.0000	0.0040	0.0080	0.0120	0.0159	0.0199	0.0239	0.0279	0.0319	0.0359
0.1	0.0398	0.0438	0.0478	0.0517	0.0557	0.0596	0.0636	0.0678	0.0714	0.0753
0.2	0.0793	0.0832	0.0871	0.0910	0.0948	0.0987	0.1026	0.1064	0.1103	0.1141
0.3	0.1179	0.1217	0.1255	0.1293	0.1331	0.1388	0.1406	0.1443	0.1480	0.1517
0.4	0.1554	0.1591	0.1628	0.1664	0.1700	0.1736	0.1772	0.1808	0.1844	0.1879
0.5	0.1915	0.1950	0.1985	0.2019	0.2054	0.2086	0.2123	0.2157	0.2190	0.2224
0.6	0.2257	0.2291	0.2324	0.2357	0.2389	0.2422	0.2454	0.2486	0.2517	0.2549
0.7	0.2580	0.2611	0.2642	0.2673	0.2704	0.2734	0.2760	0.2794	0.2823	0.2852
0.8	0.2881	0.2910	0.2939	0.2967	0.2995	0.3023	0.3051	0.3078	0.3106	0.3133
0.9	0.3159	0.3186	0.3212	0.3238	0.3264	0.3289	0.3315	0.3340	0.3365	0.3389
1.0	0.3413	0.3438	0.3451	0.3485	0.3508	0.3531	0.3554	0.3577	0.3599	0.3621
1.1	0.3643	0.3665	0.3686	0.3708	0.3729	0.3749	0.3770	0.3790	0.3810	0.3830
1.2	0.3849	0.3869	0.3888	0.3907	0.3925	0.3944	0.3962	0.3980	0.3997	0.4015
1.3	0.4032	0.4049	0.4066	0.4082	0.4099	0.4115	0.4131	0.4147	0.4162	0.4177
1.4	0.4192	0.4207	0.4222	0.4236	0.4251	0.4265	0.4279	0.4292	0.4306	0.4319
1.5	0.4332	0.4345	0.4357	0.4370	0.4382	0.4394	0.4406	0.4418	0.4430	0.4441
1.6	0.4452	0.4463	0.4474	0.4484	0.4495	0.4505	0.4515	0.4525	0.4535	0.4545
1.7	0.4554	0.4564	0.4573	0.4582	0.4591	0.4599	0.4608	0.4616	0.4625	0.4633
1.8	0.4641	0.4649	0.4656	0.4664	0.4671	0.4678	0.4686	0.4693	0.4699	0.4706
1.9	0.4713	0.4719	0.4726	0.4732	0.4738	0.4744	0.4750	0.4756	0.4762	0.4767
2.0	0.4772	0.4778	0.4783	0.4785	0.4793	0.4798	0.4803	0.4808	0.4812	0.4817
2.1	0.4821	0.4826	0.4830	0.4834	0.4838	0.4842	0.4846	0.4850	0.4854	0.4857
2.2	0.4861	0.4864	0.4868	0.4871	0.4875	0.4878	0.4881	0.4884	0.4887	0.4890
2.3	0.4893	0.4896	0.4898	0.4901	0.4904	0.4906	0.4909	0.4911	0.4913	0.4916
2.4	0.4918	0.4920	0.4922	0.4925	0.4927	0.4929	0.4931	0.4932	0.4934	0.4936
2.5	0.4938	0.4940	0.4941	0.4943	0.4945	0.4946	0.4948	0.4949	0.4951	0.4952
2.6	0.4953	0.4955	0.4956	0.4957	0.4959	0.4960	0.4961	0.4962	0.4963	0.4964
2.7	0.4965	0.4966	0.4967	0.4968	0.4969	0.4970	0.4971	0.4972	0.4973	0.4974
2.8	0.4974	0.4975	0.4976	0.4977	0.4977	0.4978	0.4979	0.4980	0.4980	0.4981
2.9	0.4981	0.4982	0.4982	0.4983	0.4984	0.4984	0.4985	0.4985	0.4986	0.4986
3.0	0.4987	0.4987	0.4987	0.4988	0.4988	0.4989	0.4989	0.4989	0.4990	0.4990
3.1	0.4990	0.4991	0.4991	0.4991	0.4992	0.4992	0.4992	0.4992	0.4993	0.4993
3.2	0.4993	0.4993	0.4994	0.4994	0.4994	0.4994	0.4994	0.4995	0.4995	0.4995
3.3	0.4995	0.4995	0.4995	0.4996	0.4996	0.4996	0.4996	0.4996	0.4996	0.4997
3.4	0.4997	0.4997	0.4997	0.4997	0.4997	0.4997	0.4997	0.4997	0.4997	0.4998
3.5	0.4998	0.4998	0.4998	0.4998	0.4998	0.4998	0.4998	0.4998	0.4998	0.4998
3.6	0.4998	0.4998	0.4999	0.4999	0.4999	0.4999	0.4999	0.4999	0.4999	0.4999
3.7	0.4999	0.4999	0.4999	0.4999	0.4999	0.4999	0.4999	0.4999	0.4999	0.4999
3.8	0.4999	0.4999	0.4999	0.4999	0.4999	0.4999	0.4999	0.4999	0.4999	0.4999
3.9	0.5000	0.5000	0.5000	0.5000	0.5000	0.5000	0.5000	0.5000	0.5000	0.5000

Student's t distribution

Percentile values (t_p) for Student's t distribution with v degrees of freedom (shaded area = p)

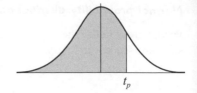

v	$t_{0.995}$	$t_{0.99}$	$t_{0.975}$	$t_{0.95}$	$t_{0.90}$	$t_{0.80}$	$t_{0.75}$	$t_{0.70}$	$t_{0.60}$	$t_{0.55}$
1	63.66	31.82	12.71	6.31	3.08	1.376	1.000	0.727	0.325	0.158
2	9.92	6.96	4.30	2.92	1.89	1.061	0.816	0.617	0.289	0.142
3	5.84	4.54	3.18	2.35	1.64	0.978	0.765	0.584	0.277	0.137
4	4.60	3.75	2.78	2.13	1.53	0.941	0.741	0.569	0.271	0.134
5	4.03	3.36	2.57	2.02	1.48	0.920	0.727	0.559	0.267	0.132
6	3.71	3.14	2.45	1.94	1.44	0.906	0.718	0.553	0.265	0.131
7	3.50	3.00	2.36	1.90	1.42	0.896	0.711	0.549	0.263	0.130
8	3.36	2.90	2.31	1.86	1.40	0.889	0.706	0.546	0.262	0.130
9	3.25	2.82	2.26	1.83	1.38	0.883	0.703	0.543	0.261	0.129
10	3.17	2.76	2.23	1.81	1.37	0.879	0.700	0.542	0.260	0.129
11	3.11	2.72	2.20	1.80	1.36	0.876	0.697	0.540	0.260	0.129
12	3.06	2.68	2.18	1.78	1.36	0.873	0.695	0.539	0.259	0.128
13	3.01	2.65	2.16	1.77	1.35	0.870	0.694	0.538	0.259	0.128
14	2.98	2.62	2.14	1.76	1.34	0.868	0.692	0.537	0.258	0.128
15	2.95	2.60	2.13	1.75	1.34	0.866	0.691	0.536	0.258	0.128
16	2.92	2.58	2.12	1.75	1.34	0.865	0.690	0.535	0.258	0.128
17	2.90	2.57	2.11	1.74	1.33	0.863	0.689	0.534	0.257	0.128
18	2.88	2.55	2.10	1.73	1.33	0.862	0.688	0.534	0.257	0.127
19	2.86	2.54	2.09	1.73	1.33	0.861	0.688	0.533	0.257	0.127
20	2.84	2.53	2.09	1.72	1.32	0.860	0.687	0.533	0.257	0.127
21	2.83	2.52	2.08	1.72	1.32	0.859	0.686	0.532	0.257	0.127
22	2.82	2.51	2.07	1.72	1.32	0.858	0.686	0.532	0.256	0.127
23	2.81	2.50	2.07	1.71	1.32	0.858	0.685	0.532	0.256	0.127
24	2.80	2.49	2.06	1.71	1.32	0.857	0.685	0.531	0.256	0.127
25	2.79	2.48	2.06	1.71	1.32	0.856	0.684	0.531	0.256	0.127
26	2.78	2.48	2.06	1.71	1.32	0.856	0.684	0.531	0.256	0.127
27	2.77	2.47	2.05	1.70	1.31	0.855	0.684	0.531	0.256	0.127
28	2.76	2.47	2.05	1.70	1.31	0.855	0.683	0.530	0.256	0.127
29	2.76	2.46	2.04	1.70	1.31	0.854	0.683	0.530	0.256	0.127
30	2.75	2.46	2.04	1.70	1.31	0.854	0.683	0.530	0.256	0.127
40	2.70	2.42	2.02	1.68	1.30	0.851	0.681	0.529	0.255	0.126
60	2.66	2.39	2.00	1.67	1.30	0.848	0.679	0.527	0.254	0.126
120	2.62	2.36	1.98	1.66	1.29	0.845	0.677	0.526	0.254	0.126
∞	2.58	2.33	1.96	1.645	1.28	0.842	0.674	0.524	0.253	0.126

Sign test (critical values)

n	$\alpha_1 = 5\%$ $\alpha_2 = 10\%$	$2\frac{1}{2}\%$ 5%	1% 2%	$\frac{1}{2}\%$ 1%	n	$\alpha_1 = 5\%$ $\alpha_2 = 10\%$	$2\frac{1}{2}\%$ 5%	1% 2%	$\frac{1}{2}\%$ 1%
1	–	–	–	–	26	8	7	6	6
2	–	–	–	–	27	8	7	7	6
3	–	–	–	–	28	9	8	7	6
4	–	–	–	–	29	9	8	7	7
5	0	–	–	–	30	10	9	8	7
6	0	0	–	–	31	10	9	8	7
7	0	0	0	–	32	10	9	8	8
8	1	0	0	0	33	11	10	9	8
9	1	1	0	0	34	11	10	9	9
10	1	1	0	0	35	12	11	10	9
11	2	1	1	0	36	12	11	10	9
12	2	2	1	1	37	13	12	10	10
13	3	2	1	1	38	13	12	11	10
14	3	2	2	1	39	13	12	11	11
15	3	3	2	2	40	14	13	12	11
16	4	3	2	2	41	14	13	12	11
17	4	4	3	2	42	15	14	13	12
18	5	4	3	3	43	15	14	13	12
19	5	4	4	3	44	16	15	13	13
20	5	5	4	3	45	16	15	14	13
21	6	5	4	4	46	16	15	14	13
22	6	5	5	4	47	17	16	15	14
23	7	6	5	4	48	17	16	15	14
24	7	6	5	5	49	18	17	15	15
25	7	7	6	5	50	18	17	16	15

Wilcoxon signed-rank test (critical values)

n	$\alpha_1 = 5\%$ $\alpha_2 = 10\%$	$2\frac{1}{2}\%$ 5%	1% 2%	$\frac{1}{2}\%$ 1%	n	$\alpha_1 = 5\%$ $\alpha_2 = 10\%$	$2\frac{1}{2}\%$ 5%	1% 2%	$\frac{1}{2}\%$ 1%
1	–	–	–	–	26	110	98	84	75
2	–	–	–	–	27	119	107	92	83
3	–	–	–	–	28	130	116	101	91
4	–	–	–	–	29	140	126	110	100
5	0	–	–	–	30	151	137	120	109
6	2	0	–	–	31	163	147	130	118
7	3	2	0	–	32	175	159	140	128
8	5	3	1	0	33	187	170	151	138
9	8	5	3	1	34	200	182	162	148
10	10	8	5	3	35	213	195	173	159
11	13	10	7	5	36	227	208	185	171
12	17	13	9	7	37	241	221	198	182
13	21	17	12	9	38	256	235	211	194
14	25	21	15	12	39	271	249	224	207
15	30	25	19	15	40	286	264	238	220
16	35	29	23	19	41	302	279	252	233
17	41	34	27	23	42	319	294	266	247
18	47	40	32	27	43	336	310	281	261
19	53	46	37	32	44	353	327	296	276
20	60	52	43	37	45	371	343	312	291
21	67	58	49	42	46	389	361	328	307
22	75	65	55	48	47	407	378	345	322
23	83	73	62	54	48	426	396	362	339
24	91	81	69	61	49	446	415	379	355
25	100	89	76	68	50	466	434	397	373

Mann-Whitney test (critical values)

n_1	n_2	$\alpha_1 =$ 5% $\alpha_2 =$ 10%	$2\frac{1}{2}\%$ 5%	1% 2%	$\frac{1}{2}\%$ 1%
2	2	–	–	–	–
2	3	–	–	–	–
2	4	–	–	–	–
2	5	0	–	–	–
2	6	0	–	–	–
2	7	0	–	–	–
2	8	1	0	–	–
2	9	1	0	–	–
2	10	1	0	–	–
2	11	1	0	–	–
2	12	2	1	–	–
2	13	2	1	0	–
2	14	3	1	0	–
2	15	3	1	0	–
2	16	3	1	0	–
2	17	3	2	0	–
2	18	4	2	0	–
2	19	4	2	1	0
2	20	4	2	1	0
3	3	0	–	–	–
3	4	0	–	–	–
3	5	1	0	–	–
3	6	2	1	–	–
3	7	2	1	0	–
3	8	3	2	0	–
3	9	4	2	1	0
3	10	4	3	1	0
3	11	5	3	1	0
3	12	5	4	2	1
3	13	6	4	2	1
3	14	7	5	2	1
3	15	7	5	3	2
3	16	8	6	3	2
3	17	9	6	4	2
3	18	9	7	4	2
3	19	10	7	4	3
3	20	11	8	5	3
4	4	1	0	–	–
4	5	2	1	0	–
4	6	3	2	1	0
4	7	4	3	1	0
4	8	5	4	2	1
4	9	6	4	3	1
4	10	7	5	3	2
4	11	8	6	4	2
4	12	9	7	5	3
4	13	10	8	5	3
4	14	11	9	6	4
4	15	12	10	7	5
4	16	14	11	7	5

n_1	n_2	$\alpha_1 =$ 5% $\alpha_2 =$ 10%	$2\frac{1}{2}\%$ 5%	1% 2%	$\frac{1}{2}\%$ 1%
4	17	15	11	8	6
4	18	16	12	9	6
4	19	17	13	9	7
4	20	18	14	10	8
5	5	4	2	1	0
5	6	5	3	2	1
5	7	6	5	3	1
5	8	8	6	4	2
5	9	9	7	5	3
5	10	11	8	6	4
5	11	12	9	7	5
5	12	13	11	8	6
5	13	15	12	9	7
5	14	16	13	10	7
5	15	18	14	11	8
5	16	19	15	12	9
5	17	20	17	13	10
5	18	22	18	14	11
5	19	23	19	15	12
5	20	25	20	16	13
6	6	7	5	3	2
6	7	8	6	4	3
6	8	10	8	6	4
6	9	12	10	7	5
6	10	14	11	8	6
6	11	16	13	9	7
6	12	17	14	11	9
6	13	19	16	12	10
6	14	21	17	13	11
6	15	23	19	15	12
6	16	25	21	16	13
6	17	26	22	18	15
6	18	28	24	19	16
6	19	30	25	20	17
6	20	32	27	22	18
7	7	11	8	6	4
7	8	13	10	7	6
7	9	15	12	9	7
7	10	17	14	11	9
7	11	19	16	12	10
7	12	21	18	14	12
7	13	24	20	16	13
7	14	26	22	17	15
7	15	28	24	19	16
7	16	30	26	21	18
7	17	33	28	23	19
7	18	35	30	24	21
7	19	37	32	26	22
7	20	39	34	28	24

n_1	n_2	$\alpha_1 =$ 5% $\alpha_2 =$ 10%	$2\frac{1}{2}\%$ 5%	1% 2%	$\frac{1}{2}\%$ 1%
8	8	15	13	9	7
8	9	18	15	11	9
8	10	20	17	13	11
8	11	23	19	15	13
8	12	26	22	17	15
8	13	28	24	20	17
8	14	31	26	22	18
8	15	33	29	24	20
8	16	36	31	26	22
8	17	39	34	28	24
8	18	41	36	30	26
8	19	44	38	32	28
8	20	47	41	34	30
9	9	21	17	14	11
9	10	24	20	16	13
9	11	27	23	18	16
9	12	30	26	21	18
9	13	33	28	23	20
9	14	36	31	26	22
9	15	39	34	28	24
9	16	42	37	31	27
9	17	45	39	33	29
9	18	48	42	36	31
9	19	51	45	38	33
9	20	54	48	40	36
10	10	27	23	19	16
10	11	31	26	22	18
10	12	34	29	24	21
10	13	37	33	27	24
10	14	41	36	30	26
10	15	44	39	33	29
10	16	48	42	36	31
10	17	51	45	38	34
10	18	55	48	41	37
10	19	58	52	44	39
10	20	62	55	47	42
11	11	34	30	25	21
11	12	38	33	28	24
11	13	42	37	31	27
11	14	46	40	34	30
11	15	50	44	37	33
11	16	54	47	41	36
11	17	57	51	44	39
11	18	61	55	47	42
11	19	65	58	50	45
11	20	69	62	53	48
12	12	42	37	31	27
12	13	47	41	35	31

n_1	n_2	$\alpha_1 =$ 5% $\alpha_2 =$ 10%	$2\frac{1}{2}\%$ 5%	1% 2%	$\frac{1}{2}\%$ 1%
12	14	51	45	38	34
12	15	55	49	42	37
12	16	60	53	46	41
12	17	64	57	49	44
12	18	68	61	53	47
12	19	72	65	56	51
12	20	77	69	60	54
13	13	51	45	39	34
13	14	56	50	43	38
13	15	61	54	47	42
13	16	65	59	51	45
13	17	70	63	55	49
13	18	75	67	59	53
13	19	80	72	63	57
13	20	84	76	67	60
14	14	61	55	47	42
14	15	66	59	51	46
14	16	71	64	56	50
14	17	77	69	60	54
14	18	82	74	65	58
14	19	87	78	69	63
14	20	92	83	73	67
15	15	72	64	56	51
15	16	77	70	61	55
15	17	83	75	66	60
15	18	88	80	70	64
15	19	94	85	75	69
15	20	100	90	80	73
16	16	83	75	66	60
16	17	89	81	71	65
16	18	95	86	76	70
16	19	101	92	82	74
16	20	107	98	87	79
17	17	96	87	77	70
17	18	102	92	82	75
17	19	109	99	88	81
17	20	115	105	93	86
18	18	109	99	88	81
18	19	116	106	94	87
18	20	123	112	100	92
19	19	123	112	101	93
19	20	130	119	107	99
20	20	138	127	114	105

Chi-square distribution

Percentile values (x_p^2) for the Chi-square distribution with v degrees of freedom.

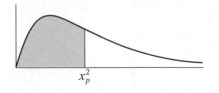

v	$\chi^2_{0.995}$	$\chi^2_{0.99}$	$\chi^2_{0.975}$	$\chi^2_{0.95}$	$\chi^2_{0.90}$	$\chi^2_{0.75}$	$\chi^2_{0.50}$	$\chi^2_{0.25}$	$\chi^2_{0.10}$	$\chi^2_{0.05}$	$\chi^2_{0.025}$	$\chi^2_{0.01}$	$\chi^2_{0.005}$
1	7.88	6.63	5.02	3.84	2.71	1.32	0.455	0.102	0.0158	0.0039	0.0010	0.0002	0.0000
2	10.6	9.21	7.38	5.99	4.61	2.77	1.39	0.575	0.211	0.103	0.0506	0.0201	0.0100
3	12.8	11.3	9.35	7.81	6.25	4.11	2.37	1.21	0.584	0.352	0.216	0.115	0.072
4	14.9	13.3	11.1	9.49	7.78	5.39	3.36	1.92	1.06	0.711	0.484	0.297	0.207
5	16.7	15.1	12.8	11.1	9.24	6.63	4.35	2.67	1.61	1.15	0.831	0.554	0.412
6	18.5	16.8	14.4	12.6	10.6	7.84	5.35	3.45	2.20	1.64	1.24	0.872	0.676
7	20.3	18.5	16.0	14.1	12.0	9.04	6.35	4.25	2.83	2.17	1.69	1.24	0.989
8	22.0	20.1	17.5	15.5	13.4	10.2	7.34	5.07	3.49	2.73	2.18	1.65	1.34
9	23.6	21.7	19.0	16.9	14.7	11.4	8.34	5.90	4.17	3.33	2.70	2.09	1.73
10	25.2	23.2	20.5	18.3	16.0	12.5	9.34	6.74	4.87	3.94	3.25	2.56	2.16
11	26.8	24.7	21.9	19.7	17.3	13.7	10.3	7.58	5.58	4.57	3.82	3.05	2.60
12	28.3	26.2	23.3	21.0	18.5	14.8	11.3	8.44	6.30	5.23	4.40	3.57	3.07
13	29.8	27.7	24.7	22.4	19.8	16.0	12.3	9.30	7.04	5.89	5.01	4.11	3.57
14	31.3	29.1	26.1	23.7	21.1	17.1	13.3	10.2	7.79	6.57	5.63	4.66	4.07
15	32.8	30.6	27.5	25.0	22.3	18.2	14.3	11.0	8.55	7.26	6.26	5.23	4.60
16	34.3	32.0	28.8	26.3	23.5	19.4	15.3	11.9	9.31	7.96	6.91	5.81	5.14
17	35.7	33.4	30.2	27.6	24.8	20.5	16.3	12.8	10.1	8.67	7.56	6.41	5.70
18	37.2	34.8	31.5	28.9	26.0	21.6	17.3	13.7	10.9	9.39	8.23	7.01	6.26
19	38.6	36.2	32.9	30.1	27.2	22.7	18.3	14.6	11.7	10.1	8.91	7.63	6.84
20	40.0	37.6	34.4	31.4	28.4	23.8	19.3	15.5	12.4	10.9	9.59	8.26	7.43
21	41.4	38.9	35.5	32.7	29.6	24.9	20.3	16.3	13.2	11.6	10.3	8.90	8.03
22	42.8	40.3	36.8	33.9	30.8	26.0	21.3	17.2	14.0	12.3	11.0	9.54	8.64
23	44.2	41.6	38.1	35.2	32.0	27.1	22.3	18.1	14.8	13.1	11.7	10.2	9.26
24	45.6	43.0	39.4	36.4	33.2	28.2	23.3	19.0	15.7	13.8	12.4	10.9	9.89
25	46.9	44.3	40.6	37.7	34.4	29.3	24.3	19.9	16.5	14.6	13.1	11.5	10.5
26	48.3	45.9	41.9	38.9	35.6	30.4	25.3	20.8	17.3	15.4	13.8	12.2	11.2
27	49.6	47.0	43.2	40.1	36.7	31.5	26.3	21.7	18.1	16.2	14.6	12.9	11.8
28	51.0	48.3	44.5	41.3	37.9	32.6	27.3	22.7	18.9	16.9	15.3	13.6	12.5
29	52.3	49.6	45.7	42.6	39.1	33.7	28.3	23.6	19.8	17.7	16.0	14.3	13.1
30	53.7	50.9	47.7	43.8	40.3	34.8	29.3	24.5	20.6	18.5	16.8	15.0	13.8
40	66.8	63.7	59.3	55.8	51.8	45.6	39.3	33.7	29.1	26.5	24.4	22.2	20.7
50	79.5	76.2	71.4	67.5	63.2	56.3	49.3	42.9	37.7	34.8	32.4	29.7	28.0
60	92.0	88.4	83.3	79.1	74.4	67.0	59.3	52.3	46.5	43.2	40.5	37.5	35.5
70	104.2	100.4	95.0	90.5	85.5	77.6	69.3	61.7	55.3	51.7	48.8	45.4	43.3
80	116.3	112.3	106.6	101.9	96.6	88.1	79.3	71.1	64.3	60.4	57.2	53.5	51.2
90	128.3	124.1	118.1	113.1	107.6	98.6	89.3	80.6	73.3	69.1	65.6	61.8	59.2
100	140.2	135.8	129.6	124.3	118.5	109.1	99.3	90.1	82.4	77.9	74.2	70.1	67.3

$$\chi^2 = \sum \left\{ \frac{(o-e)^2}{e} \right\}$$

where o and e are the observed and expected frequencies